Topic 9 — Chemistry of the Atmosphere

Topic 10 — Using Resources

Required Practicals

Practical Skills

Published by CGP.
From original material by Richard Parsons.

Editors: Emma Clayton, Emily Forsberg, Rob Hayman, Paul Jordin, George Wright.
Contributors: Barrie Crowther and Paddy Gannon.

With thanks to Sarah Pattison and Jamie Sinclair for the proofreading.
With thanks to Emily Smith for the copyright research.

ISBN: 978 1 78908 489 4

Printed by Elanders Ltd, Newcastle upon Tyne.
Clipart from Corel®
Illustrations by: Sandy Gardner Artist, email sandy@sandygardner.co.uk

Text, design, layout and original illustrations © Coordination Group Publications Ltd (CGP) 2020

The Scientific Method

Developing Theories

Come up with hypothesis

↓

Test hypothesis

↓

Evidence is peer-reviewed

↓

If all evidence backs up hypothesis, it becomes an accepted theory.

HYPOTHESIS — a possible explanation for an observation.

PEER REVIEW — when other scientists check results and explanations before they're published.

Accepted theories can still change over time as more evidence is found, e.g. the theory of atomic structure:

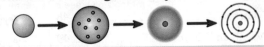

Models

REPRESENTATIONAL MODELS — a simplified description or picture of the real system, e.g. the different ways of showing covalent bonding:

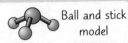

Dot and cross model

Ball and stick model

Models help scientists explain observations and make predictions.

COMPUTATIONAL MODELS — computers are used to simulate complex processes.

Issues in Science

Scientific developments can create four issues:

1. Economic — e.g. beneficial technology, like catalytic converters, may be too expensive to use.

2. Environmental — e.g. human activity could affect the natural environment.

3. Social — decisions based on research can affect people, e.g. taxes on fossil fuels.

4. Personal — some decisions affect individuals, e.g. a person may not want a wind farm being built near to their home.

Media reports on scientific developments may be oversimplified, inaccurate or biased.

Hazard and Risk

HAZARD — something that could potentially cause harm.

RISK — the chance that a hazard will cause harm.

Hazards associated with chemistry experiments include:

 Corrosive chemicals e.g. sulfuric acid

Faulty electrical equipment

Fire from Bunsen burners

The seriousness of the harm and the likelihood of it happening both need consideration.

Get your facts straight with CGP!

This CGP Knowledge Organiser has one mission in life —
helping you remember the key facts for AQA GCSE Chemistry.

We've boiled every topic down to the vital definitions,
facts and diagrams, making it all easy to memorise.

There's also a matching Knowledge Retriever book that'll test
you on every page. Perfect for making sure you know it all!

CGP — still the best! ☺

Our sole aim here at CGP is to produce the highest quality books —
carefully written, immaculately presented and dangerously close to being funny.

Then we work our socks off to get them out to you
— at the cheapest possible prices.

Contents

Designing & Performing Experiments

Collecting Data

Data should be...		
REPEATABLE	Same person gets same results after repeating experiment using the same method and equipment.	
REPRODUCIBLE	Similar results can be achieved by someone else, or by using a different method or piece of equipment.	
ACCURATE	Results are close to the true answer.	
PRECISE	All data is close to the mean.	

Reliable data is repeatable and reproducible.

Valid results are repeatable and reproducible and answer the original question.

Fair Tests

INDEPENDENT VARIABLE	Variable that you change.
DEPENDENT VARIABLE	Variable that is measured.
CONTROL VARIABLE	Variable that is kept the same.
CONTROL EXPERIMENT	An experiment kept under the same conditions as the rest of the investigation without anything being done to it.
FAIR TEST	An experiment where only the independent variable changes, whilst all other variables are kept the same.

A fair test

Control experiments are carried out when variables can't be controlled.

Four Things to Look Out For

1. RANDOM ERRORS — unpredictable differences caused by things like human errors in measuring.
2. SYSTEMATIC ERRORS — measurements that are wrong by the same amount each time.
3. ZERO ERRORS — systematic errors that are caused by using a piece of equipment that isn't zeroed properly.
4. ANOMALOUS RESULTS — results that don't fit with the rest of the data.

Anomalous results can be ignored if you know what caused them.

Processing Data

Calculate the mean — add together all data values and divide by number of values.

UNCERTAINTY — the amount by which a given result may differ from the true value.

$$\text{uncertainty} = \frac{\text{range}}{2}$$

largest value minus smallest value

In any calculation, you should round the answer to the lowest number of significant figures (s.f.) given.

Presenting Data

Bar Charts

Bar charts are used when independent variable is categoric or discrete.

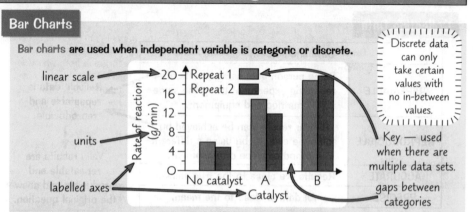

linear scale

units

labelled axes

Discrete data can only take certain values with no in-between values.

Key — used when there are multiple data sets.

gaps between categories

Plotting Graphs

Graphs are used when both variables are continuous.

Continuous data — can take any numerical value within a range.

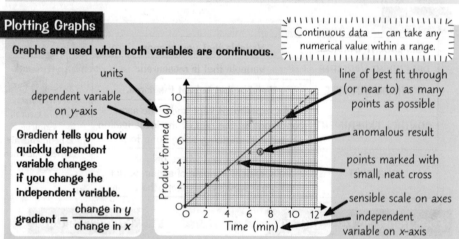

units

dependent variable on y-axis

Gradient tells you how quickly dependent variable changes if you change the independent variable.

$$\text{gradient} = \frac{\text{change in } y}{\text{change in } x}$$

line of best fit through (or near to) as many points as possible

anomalous result

points marked with small, neat cross

sensible scale on axes

independent variable on x-axis

Three Types of Correlation Between Variables

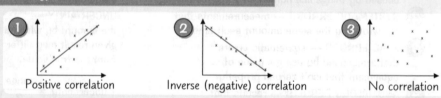

Positive correlation

Inverse (negative) correlation

No correlation

Possible reasons for a correlation:

Chance — **correlation might be a fluke.**

Third variable — **another factor links the two variables.**

Cause — **if every other variable that could affect the result is controlled, you can conclude that changing one variable causes the change in the other.**

Conclusions, Evaluations and Units

Draw conclusion by stating relationship between dependent and independent variables.

⬇

Justify conclusion using specific data.

⬇

Refer to original hypothesis and state whether data supports it.

You can only draw a conclusion from what your data shows — you can't go any further than that.

Evaluations

EVALUATION — a critical analysis of the whole investigation.

	Things to consider
Method	• Validity of method • Control of variables
Results	• Reliability, accuracy, precision and reproducibility of results • Number of measurements taken • Level of uncertainty in the results
Anomalous results	• Causes of any anomalous results

Repeating experiment with changes to improve the quality of results will give you more confidence in your conclusions.

You could make more predictions based on your conclusion, which you could test in future experiments.

S.I. Units

S.I. BASE UNITS — a set of standard units that all scientists use.

Quantity	S.I. Unit
mass	kilogram (kg)
length	metre (m)
time	second (s)
amount of a substance	mole (mol)

Scaling Units

SCALING PREFIX — a word or symbol that goes before a unit to indicate a multiplying factor.

Multiple of unit	Prefix
10^{12}	tera (T)
10^{9}	giga (G)
10^{6}	mega (M)
1000	kilo (k)
0.1	deci (d)
0.01	centi (c)
0.001	milli (m)
10^{-6}	micro (μ)
10^{-9}	nano (n)

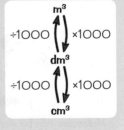

Atoms, Elements and Compounds

Atomic Structure

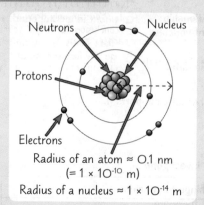

Radius of an atom ≈ 0.1 nm
$(= 1 \times 10^{-10}$ m)

Radius of a nucleus ≈ 1×10^{-14} m

Atoms have no overall charge
(number of protons =
number of electrons).

Particle	Relative mass	Relative charge
Proton	1	+1
Neutron	1	0
Electron	Very small	−1

Nuclear Symbols

NUCLEAR SYMBOL
— used to describe atoms:

Mass number = total number of
protons and neutrons in an atom

Element symbol

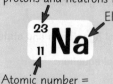

$$^{23}_{11}\text{Na}$$

Atomic number =
number of protons in an atom

Elements

There are about 100
different elements.

ELEMENTS — substances
made up of atoms with
the same atomic number.

ISOTOPES of an element — atoms
with the same number of protons
but different numbers of neutrons.

RELATIVE ATOMIC MASS (A_r) —
the average mass number for an element:

$$A_r = \frac{\text{sum of (isotope abundance} \times \text{isotope mass number)}}{\text{total abundance of all isotopes}}$$

Compounds

At least one new substance is
made in a chemical reaction.
You can usually measure an
energy change too.

COMPOUND — substance formed from two or more
elements chemically bonded together in fixed proportions.

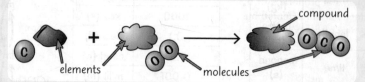

compound

elements

molecules

MOLECULE — particle containing two or more non-metal atoms bonded covalently.

Molecules can be elements (if they only have one type of atom) or compounds.

Equations, Mixtures & Chromatography

Chemical Formulas and Equations

Chemical formula — shows the proportion of atoms of each element in a compound.

E.g. CO_2 ⟵ 2 oxygen atoms for every carbon atom

Chemical equation — shows the overall change in a reaction.

	Reactants	Products
Word equation:	methane + oxygen →	carbon dioxide + water
Symbol equation:	CH_4 + $2O_2$ →	CO_2 + $2H_2O$

There must be the same number of each atom
on each side so the equation is balanced.

The large numbers in front of the formulas tell you
how many units of that element or compound there are.

Mixtures

MIXTURES — substances made
up of different elements or
compounds that aren't chemically
bonded to each other.

E.g. air is a mixture.

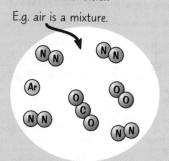

The chemical properties of a
substance aren't affected by
being part of a mixture.

Mixtures can be separated by
physical methods — these don't
involve chemical reactions or
form new substances.

Paper Chromatography

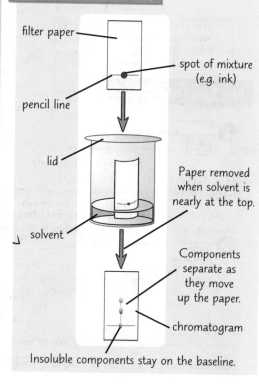

filter paper

spot of mixture
(e.g. ink)

pencil line

lid

Paper removed
when solvent is
nearly at the top.

solvent

Components
separate as
they move
up the paper.

chromatogram

Insoluble components stay on the baseline.

Topic 1 — Atomic Structure and the Periodic Table

More Separation Techniques

Filtration

FILTRATION — separates insoluble solids from liquids and solutions.

It can be used to separate out a solid product, or purify a liquid by removing insoluble impurities.

filter paper

Solid left in the filter paper.

Evaporation

EVAPORATION — separates soluble salts from solution.

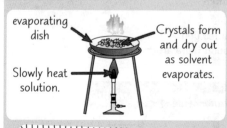

evaporating dish

Slowly heat solution.

Crystals form and dry out as solvent evaporates.

Evaporation is quick, but can't be used if the solid decomposes when heated.

Crystallisation

CRYSTALLISATION — also separates soluble salts from solution.

Heat solution, but cool it when crystals start to form.

↓

Large crystals form as solution cools.

↓

Filter out crystals and leave to dry.

Use crystallisation for salts that decompose when heated, or if you want big crystals.

Two Types of Distillation

① Simple distillation

The part with the lowest boiling point evaporates first.

Simple distillation can't separate liquids with similar boiling points, but fractional distillation can.

thermometer

water out

Vapour is cooled and condenses.

water in

heat

pure liquid

② Fractional distillation

Liquids reach the top of the column when the temperature at the top matches their boiling point.

fractionating column filled with glass rods

mixture of liquids

heat

thermometer

condenser

fractions collected separately

Topic 1 — Atomic Structure and the Periodic Table

Atomic and Electronic Structure

The History of the Atom

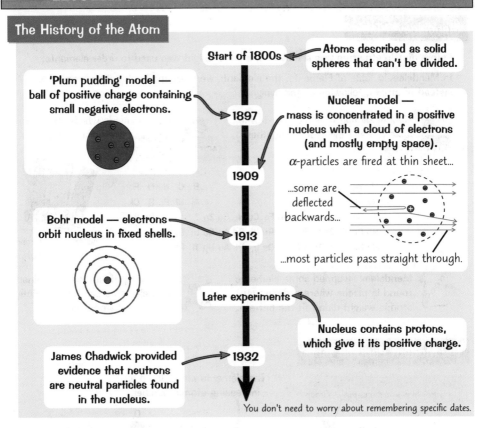

Start of 1800s — Atoms described as solid spheres that can't be divided.

'Plum pudding' model — ball of positive charge containing small negative electrons.

1897

Nuclear model — mass is concentrated in a positive nucleus with a cloud of electrons (and mostly empty space).

α-particles are fired at thin sheet...

1909

...some are deflected backwards...

Bohr model — electrons orbit nucleus in fixed shells.

1913

...most particles pass straight through.

Later experiments

Nucleus contains protons, which give it its positive charge.

James Chadwick provided evidence that neutrons are neutral particles found in the nucleus.

1932

You don't need to worry about remembering specific dates.

Electronic Structure

Electrons occupy shells — sometimes called energy levels.

Electrons fill each shell up before occupying a new one, starting with the lowest energy.

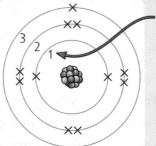

Shell	Electrons allowed in shell
1	2
2	8
3	8

Lowest energy shells are closest to the nucleus.

Electronic structure can also be represented as numbers — this one is 2, 8, 1.

Topic 1 — Atomic Structure and the Periodic Table

The Periodic Table

Mendeleev's Table

Before atomic structure was discovered, atomic weight was used to order elements.

In Mendeleev's Table of Elements, the elements were grouped using their properties, instead of strictly following atomic weight.

 Mendeleev had to leave gaps in the table to keep the groups together.

 New elements which fitted into the gaps were discovered later.

```
H
Li  Be                                      B  C  N  O  F
Na  Mg                                      Al Si P  S  Cl
K   Ca  *  Ti V  Cr Mn Fe Co Ni Cu Zn *  *  As Se Br
Rb  Sr  Y  Zr Nb Mo *  Ru Rh Pd Ag Cd In Sn Sb Te I
Cs  Ba  *  *  Ta W  *  Os Ir Pt Au Hg Tl Pb Bi
```

Mendeleev's wardrobe is less useful...

 Mendeleev swapped some elements round in places where ordering by atomic weight didn't fit the pattern.

 Discovery of isotopes explained why elements cannot be strictly ordered by atomic weight.

The Modern Periodic Table

Hydrogen is sometimes put in Group 1.

The elements are ordered by increasing atomic number.

	1	2		H												3	4	5	6	7	0 He
2	Li	Be														B	C	N	O	F	Ne
3	Na	Mg														Al	Si	P	S	Cl	Ar
4	K	Ca	Sc	Ti	V	Cr	Mn	Fe	Co	Ni	Cu	Zn	Ga	Ge	As	Se	Br	Kr
5	Rb	Sr	Y	Zr	Nb	Mo	Tc	Ru	Rh	Pd	Ag	Cd	In	Sn	Sb	Te	I	Xe
6	Cs	Ba	Lanthanides and Actinides	Hf	Ta	W	Re	Os	Ir	Pt	Au	Hg	Tl	Pb	Bi	Po	At	Rn
7	Fr	Ra																

The horizontal rows are called periods.

Elements with similar properties form vertical groups.

If you know how one element in a group reacts, you can predict how the others will react.

Position in the periodic table tells you the electronic structure:

Group number = the number of electrons in the outer shell.

Period number = the number of shells with electrons in.

Metals and Non-Metals

Reactivity of Metals and Non-Metals

METALS — elements that can form positive ions when they react.

NON-METALS — elements that don't generally form positive ions.

metals

non-metals

Atoms tend to react to form full outer shells.

	Metals	Non-metals
Get a full outer shell by...	...losing electrons	...gaining or sharing electrons
More reactive when they...	...lose electrons more easily	...gain electrons more easily
More reactive towards...	...the bottom left of the periodic table	...the top right of the periodic table

Properties of Metals and Non-Metals

	Metals	Non-metals
Appearance	Shiny	Dull
Strength	Strong but malleable	Brittle
Melting and boiling points	High	Low
Conductivity	Good electrical and thermal conductors	Poor conductors

These are general properties — they're not true for every metal or non-metal.

Transition Metals

TRANSITION METALS — metals in the centre of the periodic table.

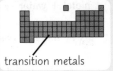

transition metals

Examples of transition metals:

Cr   Mn   Fe   Co   Ni   Cu

Transition metals have typical metal properties, but are different in three main ways:

1 They have multiple ions.

e.g. Fe^{2+} Fe^{3+}

2 They form colourful compounds.

3 They can be good catalysts.

Group 1 and Group 0 Elements

Trends in Group 1

ALKALI METALS — common name for the Group 1 metals.

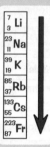

As you go DOWN Group 1:	
Reactivity	increases
Melting and boiling points	decrease
Relative atomic mass	increases

Properties of Group 1 Metals

Group 1 metals have different properties from most other metals:

 They're much more reactive.

 They're less dense and softer.

 They have lower melting points.

Compared to transition metals, Group 1 metals have a lower melting point, are more reactive and are less dense, strong and hard.

Reactions of Group 1 Elements

The Group 1 elements only have one outer electron — it doesn't take much energy to lose it so they readily form 1+ ions.

They react with a range of substances to form ionic compounds:

 metal + water → metal hydroxide + hydrogen

 metal + chlorine → metal chloride

 metal + oxygen → metal oxide

As reactivity increases down the group, the reaction with water becomes more vigorous and explosive.

Group 0 Elements

GROUP 0 ELEMENTS — non-metals with full outer shells.

Their electronic structure is stable so they are unreactive.

All Group 0 elements are colourless monatomic gases at room temperature.

As you go DOWN Group 0, the boiling point increases.

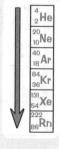

These elements are also known as the noble gases.

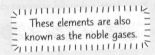

A Nobel gas

Topic 1 — Atomic Structure and the Periodic Table

Group 7 Elements

Trends in Group 7

GROUP 7 ELEMENTS — non-metals known as halogens.

Halogen	Fluorine	Chlorine	Bromine	Iodine
Appearance	yellow gas	dense green gas	volatile red-brown liquid	dark grey solid or purple vapour

As you go DOWN Group 7:	
Reactivity	decreases
Melting and boiling points	increase
Relative molecular mass	increases

$^{19}_{9}$F
$^{35.5}_{17}$Cl
$^{80}_{35}$Br
$^{127}_{53}$I
$^{210}_{85}$At

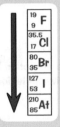

The halogens exist as diatomic molecules — two atoms joined by a covalent bond.

Reactions of Group 7 Elements

Halogens have seven outer shell electrons — they need one more electron to be filled.

They can react to fill their outer shell in two ways:

 1 Sharing electrons

Halogens form covalent bonds with other non-metals to form molecular compounds.

 2 Gaining an electron

- Halogens form ionic compounds when they react with metals.

- As they gain one electron, they form 1– ions called halides.

More reactive halogens can displace less reactive ones.

E.g. $Cl_{2(g)} + 2KBr_{(aq)} \rightarrow Br_{2(aq)} + 2KCl_{(aq)}$ ⟵ Chlorine is more reactive than bromine so displaces it from the salt.

Ions and Ionic Bonding

Ion Formation

IONS — charged particles made when electrons are transferred.

	Electron transfer	Group	Charge of ion
metals	lose electrons (form positive ions)	1	1+
		2	2+
non-metals	gain electrons (form negative ions)	6	2–
		7	1–

The ions formed by elements in these groups have the electronic structure of a noble gas.

Ionic Bonding

IONIC BONDING — the electrostatic attraction between oppositely charged ions.
Ionic bonding occurs between positive metal ions and negative non-metal ions.

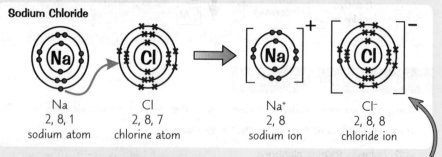

Sodium Chloride

Na	Cl	Na⁺	Cl⁻
2, 8, 1	2, 8, 7	2, 8	2, 8, 8
sodium atom	chlorine atom	sodium ion	chloride ion

Dot-cross diagrams don't show compound structure, or the size and arrangement of ions.

Three Properties of Ionic Compounds

 Giant ionic lattice structure — electrostatic forces of attraction between oppositely charged ions act in all directions.

 High melting and boiling points — lots of energy needed to overcome the many strong bonds.

 Conduct electricity only when molten or dissolved — ions free to move and carry electric charge.

Limitations:
• Model not to scale
• In reality, no gaps between ions

Limitation:
can only see outer layer of compound.

Empirical formulas of ionic compounds can be worked out from diagrams.

Covalent Bonding & Simple Molecules

Covalent Bonding

COVALENT BOND — a shared pair of electrons between two non-metal atoms.
Covalent bonding happens in non-metal compounds and in non-metal elements.

Molecular formulas show you how many atoms of each element are in a compound. **NH₃**

Dot and cross diagrams don't show relative sizes of atoms or their arrangement in space.

Ball and stick diagrams don't show which atoms the electrons in the bonds come from.

Displayed formula — doesn't show 3D structure.

Simple Molecular Substances

Covalent bonds between atoms are strong. Forces between molecules are weak.

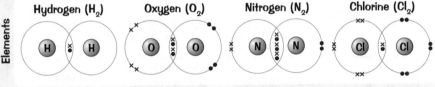

Elements

Hydrogen (H₂)   Oxygen (O₂)   Nitrogen (N₂)   Chlorine (Cl₂)

Compounds

Hydrogen Chloride (HCl)   Water (H₂O)

Ammonia (NH₃)   Methane (CH₄)

Two Properties of Simple Molecular Substances

1 Low melting and boiling points — mostly gases or liquids at room temperature.

2 Don't conduct electricity — there are no charged particles to carry charge.

As molecules get smaller, less energy is needed to break the weaker forces between them.

Covalent Structures

Polymers

POLYMERS — very long chains of repeating units.

They're usually solid at room temperature because they have relatively strong intermolecular forces.

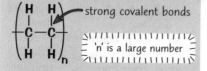

strong covalent bonds

'n' is a large number

Giant Covalent Structures

GIANT COVALENT STRUCTURES — solids containing atoms which are all bonded to each other by strong covalent bonds.

 High melting and boiling points — lots of energy needed to overcome strong covalent bonds.

 Don't conduct electricity (with a couple of exceptions) — no charged particles to carry charge.

Examples include: diamond, graphite and silicon dioxide (silica).

Carbon Allotropes

Useful in electronics and composites.

	Diamond	Graphite	Graphene
Bonding	C atoms form four covalent bonds	C atoms form three covalent bonds. No covalent bonds between layers	C atoms form three covalent bonds
Properties	Very hard	Soft, slippery	Strong, light
Melting Point	High	High	High
Conductivity	Doesn't conduct electricity	Conducts electricity and thermal energy	Conducts electricity

Each carbon atom in graphite and graphene has one delocalised electron.

FULLERENES — have hollow shapes.

rings of 6 carbon atoms (sometimes 5 or 7)

Buckminsterfullerene (C_{60}) is spherical and was the first to be discovered.

NANOTUBES — cylindrical fullerenes used in nanotechnology, electronics and materials. They have high length to diameter ratios.

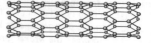

Topic 2 — Bonding, Structure and Properties of Matter

Metallic Bonding

Metallic Bonding

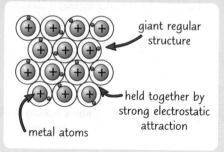

giant regular structure

held together by strong electrostatic attraction

metal atoms

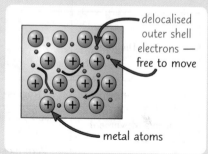

delocalised outer shell electrons — free to move

metal atoms

Four Properties of Metals

 High melting and boiling points — lots of energy needed to overcome strong metallic bonds.

 Good thermal conductors — energy transferred by delocalised electrons.

 Good electrical conductors — delocalised electrons carry charge.

 Soft and malleable — layers in metals slide over each other.

malleable metal

mailable metal

Alloys

ALLOYS — a mixture of a metal and at least one other element.

Alloys are harder than pure metals.

New element distorts layers of metal atoms — they can't slide past each other.

Topic 2 — Bonding, Structure and Properties of Matter

States of Matter and Changing State

Particle Theory

	Solid	Liquid	Gas
Particle Diagram			
Particle Arrangement	Regular	Random	Random
Particle Movement	Fixed position, vibrate	Move around each other	Move quickly in all directions
Particle Closeness	Very close together	Close together	Far apart

Particle theory doesn't show the forces between the particles.
Particles aren't solid, inelastic spheres.

Atoms don't have the bulk properties of materials.

Changes of State

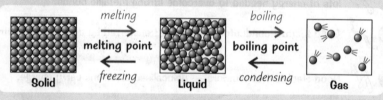

melting
melting point
freezing

boiling
boiling point
condensing

Solid   Liquid   Gas

Melting and Boiling:

Substance heats up → Particles gain energy → Forces between particles weaken → Particles break free from position

Condensing and Freezing:

Substance cools down → Particles lose energy → Forces between particles form → Particles held in position

The amount of energy needed to change state is linked to the strength of forces between particles. Stronger forces mean a higher melting and boiling point.

State Symbols

(s)	(l)	(g)	(aq)
solid	liquid	gas	aqueous

(aq)
State Symbol of East Calibama

'Aqueous' means dissolved in water.

Topic 2 — Bonding, Structure and Properties of Matter

Nanoparticles and their Uses

Particle Sizes

	Diameter (nm)
Coarse particles (PM_{10})	2500 - 10 000
Fine particles ($PM_{2.5}$)	100 - 2500
Nanoparticles	1 - 100

Coarse particles are also called dust.

contain a few hundred atoms

surface area to volume ratio = SA ÷ V

Side of cube decreases by factor of 10

SA:V increases by factor of 10

side length ÷ 10

The large surface area to volume ratio of nanoparticles means properties of nanoparticle materials may be different to those of the same materials in bulk.

Uses of Nanoparticles

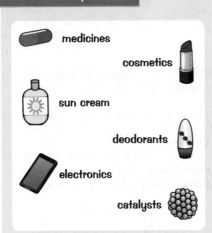

medicines

cosmetics

sun cream

deodorants

electronics

catalysts

Finding new ways to use nanoparticles is an important area of scientific research.

Evaluating Uses

Advantages
Generally more effective than equivalent products without nanoparticles.
Smaller quantities may be needed compared to materials with 'normal-sized' particles.

Disadvantages
Long-term effects on health aren't fully understood.
Could cause damage to the environment if washed away.

Mass and the Mole

Relative Formula Mass

RELATIVE FORMULA MASS (M_r) — sum of all the relative atomic masses (A_r) of the atoms in the molecular formula.

$$\text{Percentage mass of an element in a compound} = \frac{A_r \times \text{number of atoms of that element}}{M_r \text{ of the compound}} \times 100$$

Balanced Equations

BALANCED EQUATION — a symbol equation with the same number of atoms of each element on both sides.

$$2Mg + O_2 \rightarrow 2MgO$$

There are 2 magnesium atoms and 2 oxygen atoms on each side.

In a balanced equation:

Sum of the M_rs of the reactants = Sum of the M_rs of the products

The Mole

One mole = 6.02×10^{23} particles of a substance.

This is the Avogadro constant.

The particles could be e.g. atoms, molecules, ions or electrons.

Mass in grams of one mole of atoms of an element = the A_r of the element.
Mass in grams of one mole of molecules of a compound = the M_r of the compound.

$$\text{Number of moles (mol)} = \frac{\text{mass in g}}{M_r}$$

Guacamole recipe: take 6.02×10^{23} avocados...

Conservation of Mass

No atoms are created or destroyed in a chemical reaction, so the total masses of reactants and products are also the same — MASS IS CONSERVED.

If you weigh an unsealed reaction vessel, sometimes you'll see a change in mass:

DECREASE in mass — a gas is made during the reaction and escapes the vessel, so its mass is no longer accounted for.

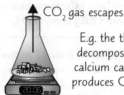

CO_2 gas escapes

E.g. the thermal decomposition of calcium carbonate produces CO_2 gas.

INCREASE in mass — a gas from the air is a reactant, so its mass is added to the mass in the vessel (none of the products are gaseous).

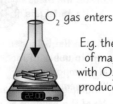

O_2 gas enters

E.g. the reaction of magnesium with O_2 gas only produces a solid.

Moles, Equations & Limiting Reactants

Moles and Equations

Balanced equations tell you how many moles of each substance take part in the reaction.

$$Mg_{(s)} + 2HCl_{(aq)} \rightarrow MgCl_{2(aq)} + H_{2(g)}$$

1 mole of Mg reacts with 2 moles of HCl

1 mole of $MgCl_2$ is made from every 2 moles of HCl

1 mole of H_2 is made for every 1 mole of $MgCl_2$

Balancing Equations Using Masses

If you know the masses of the reactants and products:

Divide mass by M_r to find the number of moles of each substance.

Divide each number of moles by the smallest number of moles.

If results aren't all whole numbers, multiply them by the same number so that they are whole.

Put these numbers in front of the chemical formulas.

Limiting Reactants

LIMITING REACTANT — a reactant that gets completely used up in a reaction, so limits the amount of product formed.

All the other reactants are in excess.

If you know the mass of the limiting reactant, you can work out the mass of a product:

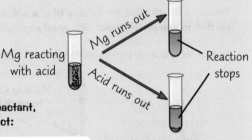

Mg reacting with acid

Mg runs out

Acid runs out

Reaction stops

Write a balanced equation for the reaction.

Divide the mass of the limiting reactant by its M_r to find the number of moles.

Use the balanced equation to find the number of moles of the product.

Multiply this number of moles by the M_r of the product to work out its mass.

You can also find the mass of a limiting reactant from the mass of a product using this method.

Topic 3 — Quantitative Chemistry

Gases and Concentrations

Gases

At the same temperature and pressure, one mole of any gas will occupy the same volume.

At room temperature and pressure, one mole of any gas occupies 24 dm³.

At r.t.p.: $\text{Volume of gas} = \dfrac{\text{Mass (in g)}}{M_r} \times 24$

(in dm³)

Room temperature and pressure (r.t.p.) = 20 °C and 1 atm

Concentration

CONCENTRATION — amount of substance dissolved in a certain volume of solution.

Increase the...	Concentration...
...amount of solute	...increases
...volume of solvent	...decreases

Two ways to measure concentration:

Concentration = ...	Units
$\dfrac{\text{mass of solute}}{\text{volume of solvent}}$	g/dm³
$\dfrac{\text{number of moles of solute}}{\text{volume of solvent}}$	mol/dm³

You can convert between these units by using the moles = mass ÷ M_r equation.

Calculating Concentration from Titrations

Titrations let you find the volume of one solution needed to completely react with another solution.

Titration experiments are often repeated — the range of these results can be used to find the uncertainty in the mean value.

To find an unknown concentration from the result of a titration:

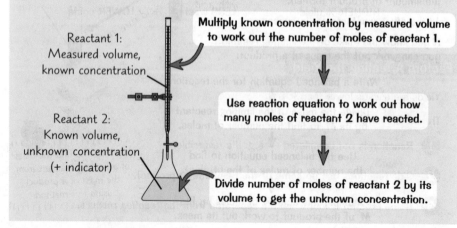

Reactant 1: Measured volume, known concentration

Reactant 2: Known volume, unknown concentration (+ indicator)

Multiply known concentration by measured volume to work out the number of moles of reactant 1.

Use reaction equation to work out how many moles of reactant 2 have reacted.

Divide number of moles of reactant 2 by its volume to get the unknown concentration.

Atom Economy and Percentage Yield

Atom Economy

ATOM ECONOMY (atom utilisation) — the percentage of
the mass of reactants that ends up as useful products.

$$\text{Atom economy} = \frac{\text{total } M_r \text{ of desired products}}{\text{total } M_r \text{ of all reactants}} \times 100$$

Three advantages of using reactions
with higher atom economies:

1. Use up resources at a slower rate.

2. Don't produce a lot of waste.

3. More profitable.

> When choosing a reaction pathway,
> the yield, rate, equilibrium position,
> atom economy and usefulness of
> by-products are all considered.

This means they are more sustainable.

Percentage Yield

YIELD — the amount of product made in a reaction.

PERCENTAGE YIELD — a comparison of the amount of product you
actually get (yield) with the maximum you could theoretically get.

$$\text{Percentage yield} = \frac{\text{mass of product actually made}}{\text{maximum theoretical mass of product}} \times 100$$

HIGHER % yield   =   LESS waste   +   LOWER costs

Factors Affecting the Yield

Yields are always lower than 100%.

Three common reasons for this:

1. Reaction is not completed — e.g. it's reversible.

2. Side reactions use up some of the reactants or product.

3. Some product is lost when it's separated from the reaction mixture.

Acids, Bases and their Reactions

The pH Scale

Alkalis are soluble bases.

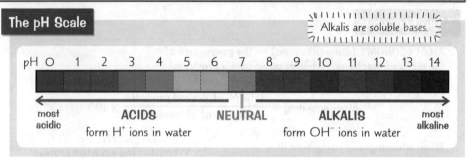

pH 0   1   2   3   4   5   6   7   8   9   10 11 12 13 14

← most acidic   ACIDS   NEUTRAL   ALKALIS   most alkaline →

form H^+ ions in water   form OH^- ions in water

Two Ways to Measure pH

(1) UNIVERSAL INDICATOR — a wide range indicator that changes colour depending on the pH. It gives an approximate pH value.

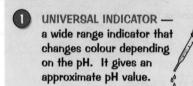

Using universal indicator gives the range of colours shown above.

(2) pH PROBE — gives an accurate value of the pH.

Neutralisation Reactions

acid + base $\Longrightarrow$ salt + water

The products of neutralisation reactions are neutral.

$$H^+_{(aq)} + OH^-_{(aq)} \Longrightarrow H_2O_{(l)}$$

Titrations

TITRATIONS (using a suitable indicator) — used to find the exact volume of acid needed to neutralise a quantity of alkali (or vice versa). The results can be used to calculate the acid or alkali concentration.

Reactions of Acids

To get the formula of a salt, balance the charges of the ions so the overall charge is neutral.

acid + metal carbonate $\Longrightarrow$ salt + water + carbon dioxide

acid + metal oxide $\Longrightarrow$ salt + water

acid + metal hydroxide $\Longrightarrow$ salt + water

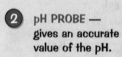

Soluble salts are made by adding metals or insoluble metal compounds to acids. The excess solid is filtered off and the remaining salt solution is crystallised.

Acid Used	Salt Produced
HCl	chloride
H_2SO_4	sulfate
HNO_3	nitrate

The first part of a salt's name comes from the positive ion in the base, alkali or carbonate.

Strong and Weak Acids

Acid Strength

	Definition	Examples
STRONG ACID	An acid that completely ionises (dissociates) in water to produce hydrogen ions.	hydrochloric acid sulfuric acid nitric acid
WEAK ACID	An acid that partially ionises (dissociates) in water to produce hydrogen ions.	ethanoic acid citric acid carbonic acid

pH and H⁺ Ion Concentration

pH — a measure of the concentration of H^+ ions in a solution.

When the pH of a solution changes by X...

...the H^+ ion concentration changes by a factor of 10^{-X}.

For a given concentration of acid, as the acid strength increases, pH decreases.

The pH of a strong acid is always less than the pH of a weaker acid at the same concentration.

Strength vs Concentration

	A measure of...
ACID STRENGTH	...the proportion of acid molecules that ionise in water.
ACID CONCENTRATION	...the number of acid molecules in a certain volume of water.

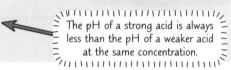

Dilute acids have a low concentration.

The pH will decrease with increasing acid concentration regardless of whether it's a strong or weak acid.

Topic 4 — Chemical Changes

Reactivity of Metals

The Reactivity Series

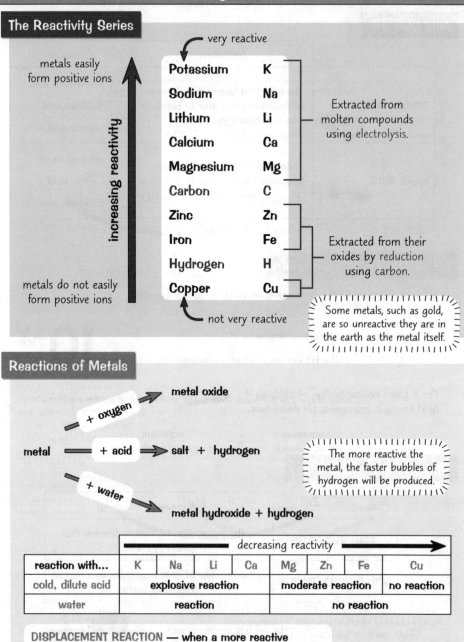

very reactive

metals easily form positive ions

increasing reactivity

Potassium	K
Sodium	Na
Lithium	Li
Calcium	Ca
Magnesium	Mg
Carbon	C
Zinc	Zn
Iron	Fe
Hydrogen	H
Copper	Cu

Extracted from molten compounds using electrolysis.

Extracted from their oxides by reduction using carbon.

metals do not easily form positive ions

not very reactive

Some metals, such as gold, are so unreactive they are in the earth as the metal itself.

Reactions of Metals

metal oxide

+ oxygen

metal ———— + acid ⟹ salt + hydrogen

+ water

metal hydroxide + hydrogen

The more reactive the metal, the faster bubbles of hydrogen will be produced.

reaction with...	K	Na	Li	Ca	Mg	Zn	Fe	Cu
	decreasing reactivity							
cold, dilute acid	explosive reaction				moderate reaction			no reaction
water	reaction				no reaction			

DISPLACEMENT REACTION — when a more reactive element displaces a less reactive metal from its compound.

Topic 4 — Chemical Changes

Redox Reactions and Ionic Equations

Redox Reactions

	Gain of...	or	Loss of...
Oxidation =	oxygen		electrons
Reduction =	electrons		oxygen

REDOX REACTION — where one substance in a reaction is reduced and another is oxidised.

Metal-acid reactions are redox reactions.

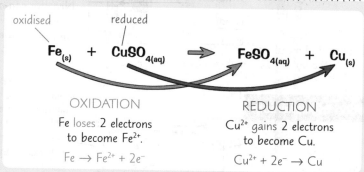

oxidised   reduced

$$Fe_{(s)} + CuSO_{4(aq)} \Rightarrow FeSO_{4(aq)} + Cu_{(s)}$$

OXIDATION
Fe loses 2 electrons to become Fe^{2+}.
$$Fe \rightarrow Fe^{2+} + 2e^-$$

REDUCTION
Cu^{2+} gains 2 electrons to become Cu.
$$Cu^{2+} + 2e^- \rightarrow Cu$$

Ionic Equations

IONIC EQUATIONS only show the particles that react and the products they form.

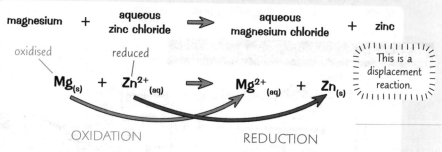

| magnesium | + | aqueous zinc chloride | → | aqueous magnesium chloride | + | zinc |

oxidised   reduced

$$Mg_{(s)} + Zn^{2+}_{(aq)} \Rightarrow Mg^{2+}_{(aq)} + Zn_{(s)}$$

This is a displacement reaction.

OXIDATION
$$Mg \rightarrow Mg^{2+} + 2e^-$$

REDUCTION
$$Zn^{2+} + 2e^- \rightarrow Zn$$

The chloride ions are spectator ions (they don't change), so they aren't shown in the equation.

Go team!

Topic 4 — Chemical Changes

Electrolysis

Electrolysis of Molten Ionic Compounds

Electrolyte — a liquid or solution that can conduct electricity because ions are free to move.

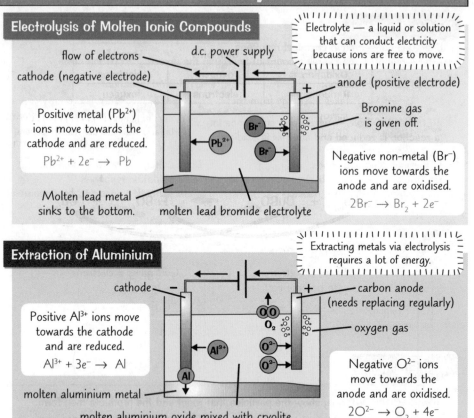

flow of electrons

d.c. power supply

cathode (negative electrode)

anode (positive electrode)

Positive metal (Pb^{2+}) ions move towards the cathode and are reduced.

$Pb^{2+} + 2e^- \rightarrow Pb$

Bromine gas is given off.

Negative non-metal (Br^-) ions move towards the anode and are oxidised.

$2Br^- \rightarrow Br_2 + 2e^-$

Molten lead metal sinks to the bottom.

molten lead bromide electrolyte

Extraction of Aluminium

Extracting metals via electrolysis requires a lot of energy.

cathode

carbon anode (needs replacing regularly)

oxygen gas

Positive Al^{3+} ions move towards the cathode and are reduced.

$Al^{3+} + 3e^- \rightarrow Al$

Negative O^{2-} ions move towards the anode and are oxidised.

$2O^{2-} \rightarrow O_2 + 4e^-$

molten aluminium metal

molten aluminium oxide mixed with cryolite (to lower the melting point)

Electrolysis of Aqueous Ionic Compounds

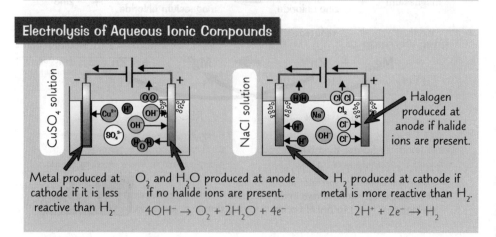

$CuSO_4$ solution

NaCl solution

Halogen produced at anode if halide ions are present.

Metal produced at cathode if it is less reactive than H_2.

O_2 and H_2O produced at anode if no halide ions are present.

$4OH^- \rightarrow O_2 + 2H_2O + 4e^-$

H_2 produced at cathode if metal is more reactive than H_2.

$2H^+ + 2e^- \rightarrow H_2$

Endothermic & Exothermic Reactions

Energy Transfer

Energy is conserved in chemical reactions.
After a reaction, the overall amount of energy in the universe is still the same.

ENDOTHERMIC reaction:

Takes in energy from the surroundings — shown by a fall in temperature.

Reactions include:
- **Thermal decompositions**
- **Citric acid + sodium hydrogencarbonate**

Use: **some sports injury packs**

EXOTHERMIC reaction:

Transfers energy to the surroundings — shown by a rise in temperature.

Reactions include:
- **Combustion**   • **Neutralisation**
- **Most oxidation reactions**

Uses: **self-heating cans and hand warmers**

Reaction Profiles

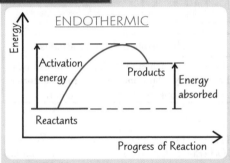

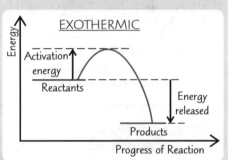

ACTIVATION ENERGY (E_a) — minimum amount of energy that reactants need to react.

Bond Energies

BOND BREAKING — ENDOTHERMIC

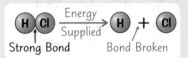

Strong Bond   Bond Broken

Endothermic reactions: **energy used to break bonds is greater than the energy released by forming new bonds.**

BOND FORMING — EXOTHERMIC

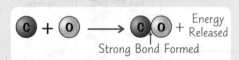

Strong Bond Formed

Exothermic reactions: **energy released by forming bonds is greater than the energy used to break existing bonds.**

overall energy change	=	total energy needed to break bonds	−	total energy released by forming new bonds

↙ These energies can be calculated from bond energies.

Cells, Batteries and Fuel Cells

Cells and Batteries

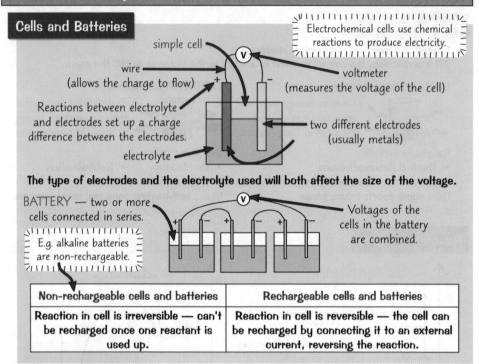

Electrochemical cells use chemical reactions to produce electricity.

simple cell

wire (allows the charge to flow)

voltmeter (measures the voltage of the cell)

Reactions between electrolyte and electrodes set up a charge difference between the electrodes.

two different electrodes (usually metals)

electrolyte

The type of electrodes and the electrolyte used will both affect the size of the voltage.

BATTERY — two or more cells connected in series.

E.g. alkaline batteries are non-rechargeable.

Voltages of the cells in the battery are combined.

Non-rechargeable cells and batteries	Rechargeable cells and batteries
Reaction in cell is irreversible — can't be recharged once one reactant is used up.	Reaction in cell is reversible — the cell can be recharged by connecting it to an external current, reversing the reaction.

Hydrogen Fuel Cells

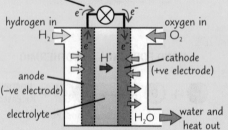

Electrical current — the flow of electrons through the external circuit.

A fuel cell uses the electrochemical oxidation of a fuel (e.g. hydrogen) to produce a potential difference.

hydrogen in H_2

oxygen in O_2

cathode (+ve electrode)

anode (–ve electrode)

electrolyte

water and heat out

Anode reaction (oxidation):

$$H_2 \rightarrow 2H^+ + 2e^-$$

Cathode reaction (reduction):

$$O_2 + 4H^+ + 4e^- \rightarrow 2H_2O$$

The overall equation is:

$$2H_2 + O_2 \rightarrow 2H_2O$$

Advantages of hydrogen fuel cells compared with batteries	Disadvantages of hydrogen fuel cells compared with batteries
Less pollution over cell's lifetime.	Storage of H_2 gas takes up more space.
Don't need recharging/replacing as often.	H_2 production can emit greenhouse gases.
Cheaper to make.	H_2 is explosive — hard to store safely.

Rates of Reaction

Comparing Rates of Reaction

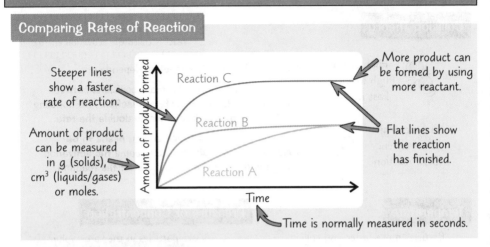

Steeper lines show a faster rate of reaction.

Amount of product can be measured in g (solids), cm^3 (liquids/gases) or moles.

More product can be formed by using more reactant.

Flat lines show the reaction has finished.

Time is normally measured in seconds.

Measuring Rates of Reaction

$$\text{Mean rate of reaction} = \frac{\text{Amount of product formed}}{\text{Time}} \quad \text{or} \quad \frac{\text{Amount of reactant used}}{\text{Time}}$$

Units depend on what has been measured — they're in the form amount/time.

Three common units of rate: g/s cm^3/s   mol/s

Using Rate Graphs

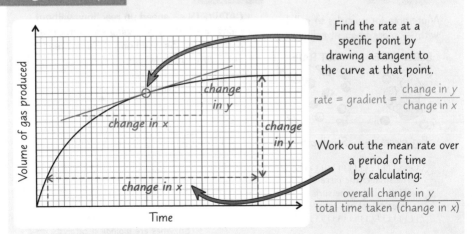

Find the rate at a specific point by drawing a tangent to the curve at that point.

$$\text{rate} = \text{gradient} = \frac{\text{change in } y}{\text{change in } x}$$

Work out the mean rate over a period of time by calculating:

$$\frac{\text{overall change in } y}{\text{total time taken (change in } x)}$$

Factors Affecting Rates of Reaction

Collision Theory

High energy
High frequency
Fast reaction

Low energy
Low frequency
Slow reaction

The minimum energy particles need to react is called the activation energy.

The rate of a chemical reaction depends on...

Collision frequency — **the more collisions between particles, the faster the rate of reaction. So doubling the frequency of collisions would double the rate.**

Collision energy — **enough energy needs to be transferred in a collision to overcome the activation energy and break the bonds to start the reaction.**

Temperature

Particles move faster and collide more frequently with more energy.

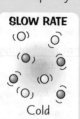

SLOW RATE
Cold

FAST RATE
Hot

Pressure or Concentration

More particles in the same volume — more frequent collisions.

SLOW RATE
Low pressure/ concentration

FAST RATE
High pressure/ concentration

Lower concentration = slower rate of revision

Surface Area

More area for particles to collide with — more frequent collisions.

SLOW RATE
Big pieces

FAST RATE
Small pieces

The smaller the piece of solid, the larger the surface area to volume ratio.

Catalysts

CATALYSTS — speed up reactions without being used up by providing an alternative pathway for the reaction. Different reactions need different catalysts.

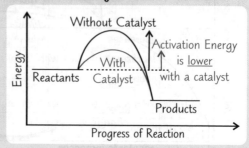

Without Catalyst

With Catalyst

Activation Energy is <u>lower</u> with a catalyst

Reactants

Products

Energy

Progress of Reaction

Enzymes are biological catalysts.

Reversible Reactions

Equilibrium

Equilibrium can only be reached when a reversible reaction takes place in a closed system (where nothing can enter or leave).

$$A + B \rightleftharpoons C + D$$

Reversible reaction — where the products can react to form the reactants again.

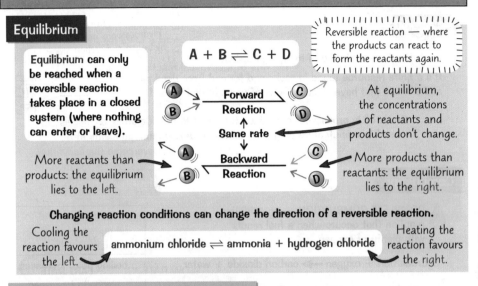

At equilibrium, the concentrations of reactants and products don't change.

More reactants than products: the equilibrium lies to the left.

More products than reactants: the equilibrium lies to the right.

Changing reaction conditions can change the direction of a reversible reaction.

Cooling the reaction favours the left.

ammonium chloride $\rightleftharpoons$ ammonia + hydrogen chloride

Heating the reaction favours the right.

Exothermic and Endothermic Reactions

If the reaction is endothermic in one direction, it will be exothermic in the other.

Hydrated copper sulfate $\underset{\text{EXOTHERMIC}}{\overset{\text{ENDOTHERMIC}}{\rule{4cm}{0.4pt}}}$ Anhydrous copper sulfate + Water

The same amount of energy is transferred in each direction.

Le Chatelier's Principle

If the conditions of a reversible reaction at equilibrium are changed, the system tries to counteract that change.

		The equilibrium shifts to favour the...
Temperature	increases	...endothermic direction to take in heat energy.
	decreases	...exothermic direction to release heat energy.
Pressure	increases	...side with fewer molecules of gas to reduce the pressure.
	decreases	...side with more molecules of gas to increase the pressure.

If concentration of a reagent is changed, the system will respond to reverse the change.

If the concentration of...	The system responds to...
...reactants increases	...make more products.
...reactants decreases	...make more reactants.

Crude Oil and Fractional Distillation

Crude Oil

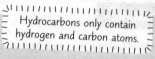

Hydrocarbons only contain hydrogen and carbon atoms.

CRUDE OIL — a mixture of many hydrocarbons.

It's a finite resource found in rocks and formed from dead plants and animals that have spent millions of years buried in mud.

#!@?%$!

Crude oil is processed to produce fuels and to provide stock chemicals used to manufacture polymers, solvents, detergents, lubricants etc.

Combustion

COMPLETE COMBUSTION — an oxidation reaction that occurs when a fuel reacts with plenty of oxygen.

hydrocarbon + oxygen ⟹ carbon dioxide + water

Hydrocarbons are used as fuels because combustion releases a lot of energy.

Hydrocarbons

As the length of the hydrocarbon chain increases, the...

...boiling point increases.

...viscosity increases.

...flammability decreases.

Fractional Distillation

FRACTIONAL DISTILLATION — a process used to separate the hydrocarbons in crude oil into fractions according to their boiling points.

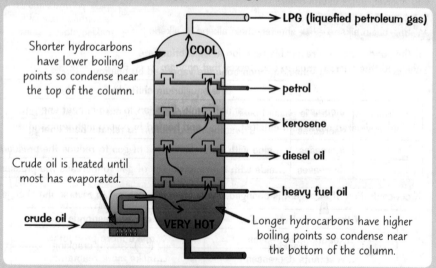

Shorter hydrocarbons have lower boiling points so condense near the top of the column.

COOL

LPG (liquefied petroleum gas)

petrol

kerosene

diesel oil

heavy fuel oil

Crude oil is heated until most has evaporated.

crude oil

VERY HOT

Longer hydrocarbons have higher boiling points so condense near the bottom of the column.

Alkanes and Cracking

Alkanes

ALKANES — the simplest type of hydrocarbon, containing only single covalent bonds (they're saturated).

Most hydrocarbons in crude oil are alkanes.

The general formula for the homologous series of alkanes is C_nH_{2n+2}.

Number of carbon atoms	1	2	3	4
Name	Methane	Ethane	Propane	Butane
Formula	CH_4	C_2H_6	C_3H_8	C_4H_{10}
Structure	H—C—H (with H above and below)	H—C—C—H (with H above and below each C)	H—C—C—C—H (with H above and below each C)	H—C—C—C—C—H (with H above and below each C)

Two Methods of Cracking

There is a high demand for fuels with shorter carbon chains.

CRACKING — breaks down long-chain hydrocarbons into shorter, more useful ones.

long-chain alkane ⟹ shorter-chain alkane + alkene

Alkenes are used to make polymers and are a starting material for making other chemicals.

Long-chain hydrocarbons are vaporised by heating.

Hydrocarbon vapour is passed over a hot powdered aluminium catalyst.

Hydrocarbon vapour is mixed with steam and heated to a very high temperature.

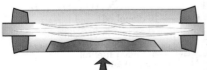

Heat

① Catalytic cracking

Heat

② Steam cracking

Topic 7 — Organic Chemistry

Alkenes and their Reactions

Alkenes

ALKENES — unsaturated hydrocarbons that have a carbon-carbon double bond (this is the functional group). The C=C double bond makes them more reactive than alkanes.

> Functional group — a group of atoms in a molecule that dictate how that molecule typically reacts.

The general formula for the alkenes is C_nH_{2n}.

Number of carbon atoms	2	3	4	5
Name	Ethene	Propene	Butene	Pentene
Formula	C_2H_4	C_3H_6	C_4H_8	C_5H_{10}
Structure	H₂C=CH₂	H₃C–CH=CH₂	e.g. H₃C–CH₂–CH=CH₂	e.g. H₃C–CH₂–CH₂–CH=CH₂

Incomplete Combustion

> Alkenes produce a smoky flame when they combust incompletely.

 INCOMPLETE COMBUSTION — when a fuel burns in air but there's not enough oxygen to burn completely.

alkene + oxygen ➔ carbon + carbon monoxide + carbon dioxide + water

Addition Reactions

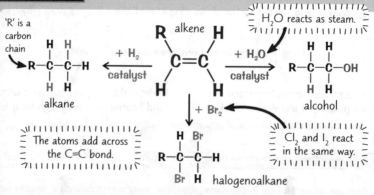

> The atoms add across the C=C bond.

> H_2O reacts as steam.

> Cl_2 and I_2 react in the same way.

'R' is a carbon chain

alkane

alcohol

halogenoalkane

Adding an alkene to bromine water causes it to change from orange to colourless.

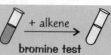

+ alkene

bromine test

Addition Polymers

Addition Polymerisation

POLYMERS — long molecules formed when lots of small molecules (monomers) join together.

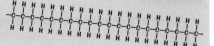

ADDITION POLYMERISATION — when molecules with C=C bonds join together in addition reactions.

Monomer   Polymer

'n' means there can be any number of monomers.

$$n \left(\begin{matrix} H & & H \\ & C=C & \\ H & & H \end{matrix} \right) \longrightarrow \left(\begin{matrix} H & H \\ | & | \\ -C-C- \\ | & | \\ H & H \end{matrix} \right)_n$$

Ethene   Poly(ethene)

Polymers are named after the monomer they're formed from.

REPEATING UNIT — the shortest repeating section of a polymer. It contains the same atoms as the monomer because no other products are formed in an addition polymerisation.

Repeating Units

Four steps for drawing the repeating unit from the monomer:

$$n \left(\begin{matrix} & H & & & H \\ & | & & & \\ H-C & -C & =C & \\ & | & | & & H \\ & H & H & & \end{matrix} \right) \longrightarrow \left(\begin{matrix} H_3C & H \\ | & | \\ -C-C- \\ | & | \\ H & H \end{matrix} \right)_n$$

Propene   Poly(propene)

To draw the monomer from the repeating unit, just reverse the method below.

① Draw the alkene carbons and replace the double bond with a single bond.

② Add an extra single bond to each carbon atom.

③ Add the other groups in the same way that they surrounded the double bond.

④ Add the brackets and 'n'.

Alcohols

Alcohols

ALCOHOLS — a compound containing an –OH functional group.

Number of carbon atoms	1	2	3	4
Name	Methanol	Ethanol	Propanol	Butanol
Formula	CH_3OH	C_2H_5OH or CH_3CH_2OH	C_3H_7OH or e.g. $CH_3CH_2CH_2OH$	C_4H_9OH or e.g. $CH_3CH_2CH_2CH_2OH$
Structure	H–C–O–H (with H above and below C)	H H H–C–C–O–H H H	H H H H–C–C–C–O–H e.g. H H H	H H H H H–C–C–C–C–O–H e.g. H H H H

Four Properties of the First Four Alcohols

1. Flammable — they undergo complete combustion in air.

   alcohol + oxygen → carbon dioxide + water

2. Soluble in water — they give neutral solutions.

3. They react with sodium to form hydrogen gas.

4. Oxidised by oxidising agents to form carboxylic acids.

Two key uses of alcohols:

 Short-chain alcohols make good fuels.

 Solvents in industry

Fermentation of Alcohols

FERMENTATION — a process where an enzyme in yeast is used to convert sugar solutions to aqueous solutions of ethanol.

sugar —yeast→ ethanol + carbon dioxide

Optimum conditions for fermentation:		
37 °C	Slightly acidic solution	Anaerobic conditions

Carboxylic Acids and Esters

Carboxylic Acids

CARBOXYLIC ACIDS — a compound containing a –COOH functional group.

Number of carbon atoms	1	2	3	4
Name	Methanoic acid	Ethanoic acid	Propanoic acid	Butanoic acid
Formula	HCOOH	CH_3COOH	C_2H_5COOH	C_3H_7COOH
Structure	H–C with O and O–H	H–C–C with H's and O, O–H	H–C–C–C chain with O–H	H–C–C–C–C chain with O–H

Reactions of Carboxylic Acids

Carboxylic acids react like any other acid. For example:

carboxylic acid + metal carbonate

↓

salt + carbon dioxide + water

Properties of Carboxylic Acids

Carboxylic acids are weak acids — they don't fully ionise when dissolved in water.

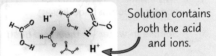

Solution contains both the acid and ions.

They have a higher pH than strong acids at the same concentration.

Esters

ESTERS — molecules formed when an alcohol reacts with a carboxylic acid.

alcohol + carboxylic acid $\xrightarrow{\text{acid catalyst}}$ ester + water

For example:

Sorry. Not you, Esther.

Ethanol + Ethanoic acid → Ethyl ethanoate + Water (H_2O)

This is the only ester you need to know. You don't have to be able to draw it.

Topic 7 — Organic Chemistry

Condensation and Natural Polymers

Condensation Polymers

CONDENSATION POLYMERS — polymers formed from monomers with two functional groups.

In condensation polymerisation, a small molecule is lost for each new bond formed.

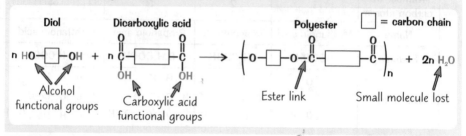

Diol   **Dicarboxylic acid**   **Polyester**   □ = carbon chain

Alcohol functional groups

Carboxylic acid functional groups

Ester link

Small molecule lost

+ 2n H$_2$O

Proteins

PROTEINS — polymers of amino acids.

Condensation polymerisation reaction

Glycine — the simplest amino acid.

Polypeptide

+ n H$_2$O

Amino group

Carboxyl group

Proteins contain different amino acids in their polymer chains, giving them different shapes and properties.

DNA

DNA (deoxyribonucleic acid) — a large molecule made up of two polymer chains of nucleotide monomers. It is essential to life.

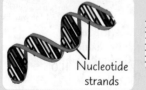

There are four different types of nucleotide monomer.

Nucleotide strands

DNA encodes genetic information that allows living organisms and viruses to develop and operate.

Starch and Cellulose

 SUGARS — small molecules containing carbon, oxygen and hydrogen.

These monomers can polymerise to form large carbohydrates, e.g.

STARCH — used by living organisms to store energy.

CELLULOSE — used to make plant cell walls.

Purity, Formulations and Gas Tests

Purity

	Everyday Definition	Chemical Definition
PURE SUBSTANCE	A substance with nothing added to it, e.g. milk.	A substance containing only one element or compound.

A chemically pure substance will:

Melt at a specific temperature.	Boil at a specific temperature.

You can test the purity of a sample by comparing its melting or boiling point with that of the pure substance.

Impurities in a sample will:
- lower the melting point and increase the melting range.
- increase the boiling point and may also increase the boiling range.

Formulations

FORMULATIONS — useful mixtures with a precise purpose.

Each component in a formulation is present in a measured quantity, and contributes to the properties of the formulation.

 metal alloys

 cleaning products

 medicines

 food

 fertilisers

 cosmetics

 paints

 fuels

Four Tests for Gases

1 HYDROGEN burns quickly with a pop.

POP!

Lighted splint

H_2 gas in open test tube

2 OXYGEN will relight a glowing splint.

Glowing splint

Oxygen gas

3 CHLORINE bleaches damp litmus paper white.

Litmus paper

Chlorine gas

4 CARBON DIOXIDE makes limewater turn cloudy when shaken with or bubbled through it.

CO_2 gas →

Limewater — an aqueous solution of calcium hydroxide

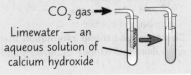

Paper Chromatography

Two Phases of Chromatography

CHROMATOGRAPHY — an analytical method used to separate the substances in a mixture. It can be used to identify the substances.

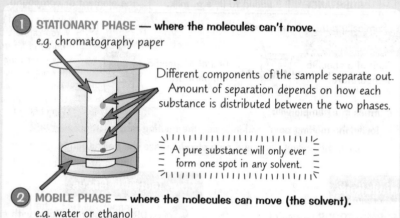

1 STATIONARY PHASE — where the molecules can't move.
e.g. chromatography paper

Different components of the sample separate out. Amount of separation depends on how each substance is distributed between the two phases.

⟋⎸⎹⎸⎹⎸⎹⎸⎹⎸⎹⎸⎹⎸⎹⎸⎹⎸⎹⎸⎹⎸⎹⎸⎹⎸⎲
A pure substance will only ever
form one spot in any solvent.
⟍⎸⎹⎸⎹⎸⎹⎸⎹⎸⎹⎸⎹⎸⎹⎸⎹⎸⎹⎸⎹⎸⎹⎸⎹⎸⎲

2 MOBILE PHASE — where the molecules can move (the solvent).
e.g. water or ethanol

| Substances dissolve in the mobile phase. | ⟹ | The mobile phase moves through the stationary phase. | ⟹ | Substances that are more soluble in the mobile phase or less attracted to the stationary phase move further. |

R_f Values

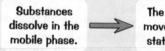

R_f VALUE — the ratio between the distance travelled by the dissolved substance and the distance travelled by the solvent.

$$R_f = \frac{\text{distance travelled by substance (B)}}{\text{distance travelled by solvent (A)}}$$

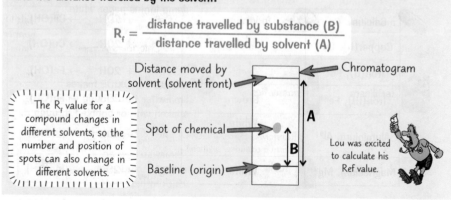

Distance moved by solvent (solvent front)

Chromatogram

⟋⎸⎹⎸⎹⎸⎹⎸⎹⎸⎹⎸⎹⎸⎹⎸⎹⎸⎹⟍
The R_f value for a
compound changes in
different solvents, so the
number and position of
spots can also change in
different solvents.
⟍⎸⎹⎸⎹⎸⎹⎸⎹⎸⎹⎸⎹⎸⎹⎸⎹⎸⎹⟋

Spot of chemical

A

B

Baseline (origin)

Lou was excited to calculate his Ref value.

Tests for Ions

Anions and Cations

ANION	An ion with a negative charge.
CATION	An ion with a positive charge.

Test for Halides

Add dilute nitric acid followed by silver nitrate solution to mystery solution.

Chloride (Cl^-) ions give a white precipitate.

silver chloride

Bromide (Br^-) ions give a cream precipitate.

silver bromide

Iodide (I^-) ions give a yellow precipitate.

silver iodide

Test for Sulfates

Add dilute hydrochloric acid followed by barium chloride solution to mystery solution.

If sulfate (SO_4^{2-}) ions are present, a white precipitate will form.

barium sulfate precipitate

Test for Carbonates

Add a couple of drops of dilute acid.

↓

Connect the test tube to a test tube of limewater.

↓

Carbonate ions react to form carbon dioxide, which will turn the limewater cloudy.

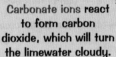

Test for Metal Cations with NaOH

Add a few drops of sodium hydroxide **(NaOH) solution to mystery solution.**

Metal Ion	Colour of Precipitate	Ionic Equation
Calcium, Ca^{2+}	White	$Ca^{2+}_{(aq)} + 2OH^-_{(aq)} \rightarrow Ca(OH)_{2(s)}$
Copper(II), Cu^{2+}	Blue	$Cu^{2+}_{(aq)} + 2OH^-_{(aq)} \rightarrow Cu(OH)_{2(s)}$
Iron(II), Fe^{2+}	Green	$Fe^{2+}_{(aq)} + 2OH^-_{(aq)} \rightarrow Fe(OH)_{2(s)}$
Iron(III), Fe^{3+}	Brown	$Fe^{3+}_{(aq)} + 3OH^-_{(aq)} \rightarrow Fe(OH)_{3(s)}$
Aluminium, Al^{3+}	White (Redissolves in excess NaOH to form a colourless solution.)	$Al^{3+}_{(aq)} + 3OH^-_{(aq)} \rightarrow Al(OH)_{3(s)}$
Magnesium, Mg^{2+}	White	$Mg^{2+}_{(aq)} + 2OH^-_{(aq)} \rightarrow Mg(OH)_{2(s)}$

Flame Tests and Spectroscopy

Flame Tests for Metal Cations

Lithium ions	Sodium ions	Potassium ions	Calcium ions	Copper ions
Li^+	Na^+	K^+	Ca^{2+}	Cu^{2+}
crimson flame	yellow flame	lilac flame	orange-red flame	green flame

Disadvantage of flame tests — if the sample contains a mixture of metal ions, the flame colours of some ions may be hidden by the colours of others.

Three Advantages of Instrumental Analysis

INSTRUMENTAL ANALYSIS — using machines to analyse unknown substances.

1. Sensitive — can detect even the tiniest amounts
2. Fast — tests can be automated
3. Accurate

Two Uses of Flame Emission Spectroscopy

Flame emission spectroscopy is an example of instrumental analysis.

Sample heated in a flame.	Light analysed in a spectroscope.	A line spectrum of different wavelengths of light is produced.

Line spectra can be used to:

If multiple ions are present in a sample, the spectrum will be a combination of all their individual spectra.

1. Identify ions in solution — each ion has a unique line spectrum.
2. Determine the concentration of ions — this can be calculated from the intensity of the lines.

Topic 8 — Chemical Analysis

The Evolution of the Atmosphere

Volcanic Gases

Intense volcanic activity released gases.

Nitrogen built up over time.

The early atmosphere probably contained mainly carbon dioxide and virtually no oxygen gas.

The early atmosphere was probably like those of Mars and Venus today.

Theories about Earth's early atmosphere have developed over time. They're hard to prove as it's hard to gather evidence from 4.6 billion years ago.

Absorption of Carbon Dioxide from Atmosphere

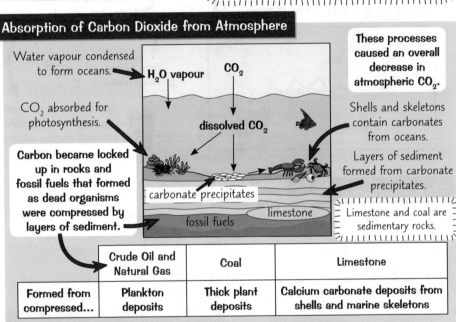

Water vapour condensed to form oceans.

CO_2 absorbed for photosynthesis.

Carbon became locked up in rocks and fossil fuels that formed as dead organisms were compressed by layers of sediment.

These processes caused an overall decrease in atmospheric CO_2.

Shells and skeletons contain carbonates from oceans.

Layers of sediment formed from carbonate precipitates.

Limestone and coal are sedimentary rocks.

	Crude Oil and Natural Gas	Coal	Limestone
Formed from compressed...	Plankton deposits	Thick plant deposits	Calcium carbonate deposits from shells and marine skeletons

Increase in Oxygen

Algae evolved ~2.7 billion years ago. Plants evolved over the next billion years.

These organisms produce oxygen by photosynthesis.

$$6CO_2 + 6H_2O \xrightarrow{light} C_6H_{12}O_6 + 6O_2$$

carbon dioxide + water → glucose + oxygen

The increase in atmospheric oxygen led to the evolution of animals.

Today

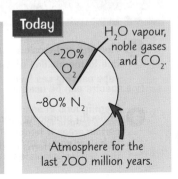

H_2O vapour, noble gases and CO_2.

~20% O_2

~80% N_2

Atmosphere for the last 200 million years.

Greenhouse Gases & Climate Change

The Greenhouse Effect

Greenhouse Gases		
carbon dioxide	methane	water vapour

GREENHOUSE EFFECT — when greenhouse gases in the atmosphere absorb long wavelength radiation and re-radiate it in all directions, including back towards Earth, helping to keep the Earth warm.

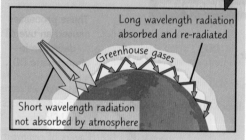

Long wavelength radiation absorbed and re-radiated

Greenhouse gases

Short wavelength radiation not absorbed by atmosphere

Human Activities

 Deforestation means less carbon dioxide is removed by photosynthesis.

Burning fossil fuels releases carbon dioxide.

Causes of increased carbon dioxide and methane

Farm animals produce methane.

 Decomposition of landfill and agricultural waste releases carbon dioxide and methane.

Climate Change Evidence

Peer reviewed evidence → Most scientists think that → increased CO$_2$ levels → have caused → the average temperature of Earth's surface to increase → and this will lead to → climate change

Global climate change is very complex and hard to model. This leads to oversimplified models and speculation in the media where stories are biased or missing information.

Four Possible Consequences of Climate Change

1 Flooding and erosion in coastal areas due to the melting of the polar ice caps causing sea levels to rise.

2 More frequent and severe storms.

3 Difficulty producing food in certain areas if temperature and rainfall patterns change.

4 Changes in the distribution of some wild species if habitats change.

Carbon Footprints and Air Pollution

Carbon Footprints

> CARBON FOOTPRINT — how much carbon dioxide and other greenhouse gases are released over something's full life cycle — e.g. a product, service or event.

- Reducing carbon dioxide and methane emissions reduces the carbon footprint.

- Actions to reduce carbon footprints may be limited if individuals and governments are unwilling or unable to make changes.

Santa worried about his carbon footprint.

Air Pollution

Fossil fuels contain hydrocarbons and sometimes sulfur impurities.

 Combustion of these fuels releases gases and particles which pollute the air.

Carbon monoxide doesn't have any colour or smell, so it's hard to detect.

Pollutant	Formation	Effects
carbon monoxide	carbon monoxide, carbon particulates, water vapour, carbon dioxide	Stops blood from transporting enough oxygen around the body — this can cause fainting, coma or death.
carbon particulates (soot)	Incomplete combustion of fossil fuels (e.g. coal).	Respiratory problems Global dimming
sulfur dioxide	Oxidation of sulfur impurities in fossil fuels during combustion.	NO$_x$ SO$_2$ damage to plants, statues and buildings Acid rain Respiratory problems
oxides of nitrogen	Reaction between nitrogen and oxygen in the air caused by the heat of burning fuels, e.g. in car engines.	

Materials

Glass and Ceramics

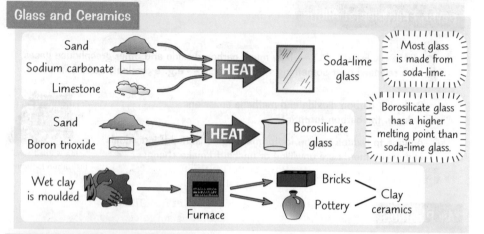

Sand
Sodium carbonate
Limestone
→ **HEAT** → Soda-lime glass

Most glass is made from soda-lime.

Sand
Boron trioxide
→ **HEAT** → Borosilicate glass

Borosilicate glass has a higher melting point than soda-lime glass.

Wet clay is moulded → Furnace → Bricks / Pottery > Clay ceramics

Four Examples of Composites

COMPOSITES — made up of a matrix or binder material surrounding reinforcement fibres or fragments.

1. Fibreglass — used for speedboats
2. Carbon fibre — used to make racing cars
3. Concrete — a building material
4. Wood — a natural composite

Polymers

Polymers have different properties depending on how they're made and what they're made from.

Polymer	How It's Made	Properties
Low density poly(ethene)	Ethene, moderate temperature, high pressure	Flexible
High density poly(ethene)	Ethene, lower temperature and pressure, with a catalyst	Rigid

Polymer properties also depend on how their chains are bonded to each other.

Polymer	Intermolecular Bonds	Properties
Thermosoftening polymers	Weak forces between individual polymer chains	Can be melted
Thermosetting polymers	Monomers form cross-links between polymer chains	Strong, hard, rigid, don't melt

Metals and Corrosion

Seven Examples of Alloys

1 Gold + Silver, Copper and Zinc ⟶ **GOLD ALLOYS** Jewellery

24 carat gold = 100% gold
18 carat gold = 75% gold

2 Copper + Zinc ⟶ **BRASS** Taps

3 Copper + Tin ⟶ **BRONZE** Medals

4 Iron + Carbon ⟶ **LOW CARBON STEEL** (easily shaped) Cars

5 Iron + Carbon ⟶ **HIGH CARBON STEEL** (strong but brittle) Bridges

6 Iron + Carbon, Chromium and Nickel ⟶ **STAINLESS STEEL** (hard, resistant to corrosion) Cutlery

7 Aluminium + Various Other Metals ⟶ **ALUMINIUM ALLOYS** (low density) Aircraft

Corrosion and Rusting

CORROSION — where metals react with substances in their environment and are gradually destroyed.

RUSTING — corrosion of iron by water and air.

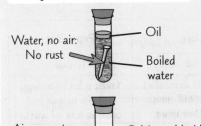

Water, no air: No rust — Oil
— Boiled water

Air, no water: No rust — Calcium chloride (absorbs water)

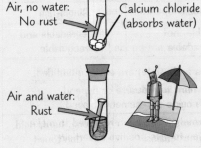

Air and water: Rust

Three Ways to Prevent Rusting

1 Barrier methods: Painting, greasing and electroplating iron to keep out water and oxygen.

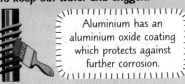

Aluminium has an aluminium oxide coating which protects against further corrosion.

2 Sacrificial method: Attaching a more reactive metal to iron.

3 Galvanisation: Both a barrier and sacrificial method. Iron is coated with a layer of more reactive zinc.

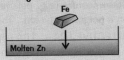

Fe

Molten Zn

Topic 10 — Using Resources

Resources & Life Cycle Assessments

Resources

Humans use natural resources for a variety of different purposes:

Fuel for heating

Shelter

Food

Clothing

Fuel for transport

We can use agricultural or synthetic products in place of certain natural resources, e.g. rubber can be replaced by man-made polymers.

Some natural resources are FINITE — they will eventually run out.

Nuclear fuel

Oil

Coal

RENEWABLE RESOURCES — resources that reform at a similar, or faster, rate than we use them, e.g. timber.

Finite resources are processed to provide materials and energy.

Life Cycle Assessments

LIFE CYCLE ASSESSMENT (LCA) — an assessment of the environmental impact of a product over each stage of its life.

Life Cycle Assessment Stage	Plastic Bag	Paper Bag
Raw Materials	Crude oil	Timber
Manufacturing and Packaging	Key compounds extracted by fractional distillation. Waste has other uses.	Takes a lot of energy to pulp timber and creates lots of waste
Using the Product	Reusable	Single-use
Product Disposal	Recyclable, not biodegradable	Biodegradable and recyclable

- Some factors (e.g. water, energy sources and waste) are easily quantified.
- Some factors (e.g. pollutant effects) are hard to measure or depend on a person's opinion. This can make life cycle assessments biased.
- SELECTIVE LCA — LCA where some information has been removed to make a product look better than it really is, often to give positive advertising.

Reuse and Recycling

Improving Sustainability

SUSTAINABLE DEVELOPMENT — meeting the needs of present society while not damaging the lives of future generations.

Three ways to improve sustainability:

 1 Reducing the amount of raw materials used

 2 Reusing products instead of throwing them away

 3 Recycling products that can't be reused

Recycling and reusing products reduces the amount of finite natural resources we need to extract, as well as the energy and waste involved in their extraction.

Copper Ores

Copper ore is a finite resource that is becoming scarce.
We can improve sustainability by extracting from low-grade ores.

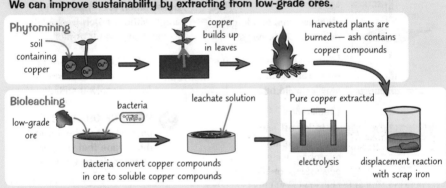

Phytomining
soil containing copper → copper builds up in leaves → harvested plants are burned — ash contains copper compounds

Bioleaching
low-grade ore → bacteria → leachate solution
bacteria convert copper compounds in ore to soluble copper compounds

Pure copper extracted
electrolysis — displacement reaction with scrap iron

Recycling Metals

Recycling metals helps to save on the large amounts of energy required to mine and extract them.

Waste metal → Melted down → Recast into new products

Amount of separation required for recyclable metals depends on the metal and final product.

Both waste steel and iron can be added to iron in a blast furnace together to reduce the amount of iron ore required.

Recycling Glass

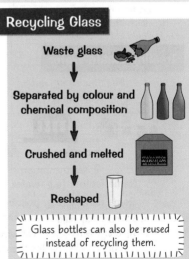

Waste glass
↓
Separated by colour and chemical composition
↓
Crushed and melted
↓
Reshaped

Glass bottles can also be reused instead of recycling them.

Treating Water

Potable Water

**POTABLE WATER —
water that is safe to drink.**

Potable water is not chemically pure. It can contain low levels of dissolved salts and microbes.

Type of Water	Source	Treatment
Ground water	Underground rocks	Must be filtered and sterilised
Salt water	Sea water	Must be desalinated
Waste water	Sewage treatment and agricultural systems	Requires a lot of treatment

Treating Ground Water

Mesh
— to remove any large debris such as twigs

Sand and gravel filtration
— to remove any smaller solid bits

Sterilisation
— to kill off any harmful bacteria or microbes using chlorine gas, ozone or UV light

This is how rainwater collected in the ground, lakes and rivers is treated in the UK.

Two Methods of Desalination

Desalination is carried out in areas without much fresh water to make sea water potable.

1 **DISTILLATION** — boiling the water to separate it from dissolved salts.

2 **REVERSE OSMOSIS** — passing the water through a membrane that only allows water molecules through.

These methods use lots of energy.

Treating Waste Water

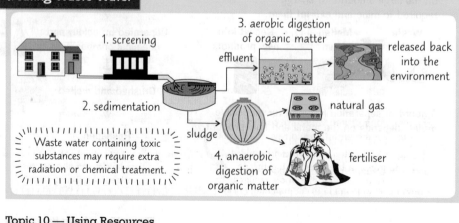

1. screening

2. sedimentation

3. aerobic digestion of organic matter

effluent

released back into the environment

sludge

natural gas

4. anaerobic digestion of organic matter

fertiliser

Waste water containing toxic substances may require extra radiation or chemical treatment.

Topic 10 — Using Resources

The Haber Process

Producing Ammonia

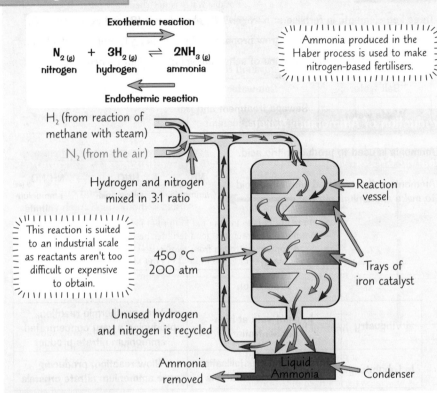

Exothermic reaction

$$N_{2\,(g)} + 3H_{2\,(g)} \rightleftharpoons 2NH_{3\,(g)}$$

nitrogen   hydrogen   ammonia

Endothermic reaction

Ammonia produced in the Haber process is used to make nitrogen-based fertilisers.

H_2 (from reaction of methane with steam)

N_2 (from the air)

Hydrogen and nitrogen mixed in 3:1 ratio

This reaction is suited to an industrial scale as reactants aren't too difficult or expensive to obtain.

450 °C
200 atm

Reaction vessel

Trays of iron catalyst

Unused hydrogen and nitrogen is recycled

Ammonia removed

Liquid Ammonia

Condenser

Reaction Conditions

	Higher Temperature	Lower Temperature	Higher Pressure	Lower Pressure
Yield	Lower	Higher	Higher	Lower
Rate	Faster	Slower	Faster	Slower

Higher temperatures would make the reaction run faster, but also favour the endothermic reverse reaction, lowering the yield.

The reaction temperature of 450 °C is a compromise between a faster rate of reaction and a higher yield.

Pressure is kept as high as possible without becoming dangerous or expensive.

Topic 10 — Using Resources

NPK Fertilisers

Key Elements

Three key elements in fertilisers: nitrogen **(N)**, phosphorus **(P)** and potassium **(K)**.

Plants need these elements to grow properly and increase agricultural productivity.

NPK FERTILISERS — formulations of salts containing the right percentages of elements to help plants grow.

Production of Ammonium Nitrate

Ammonia is used to produce nitric acid.

Ammonia is then reacted with nitric acid to make ammonium nitrate: ➡

$$NH_{3\,(aq)} + HNO_{3\,(aq)} \rightarrow NH_4NO_{3\,(aq)}$$

ammonia   nitric acid   ammonium nitrate

Ammonium nitrate is a good fertiliser because it contains nitrogen from two sources.

	Production	Result
In Industry	In giant vats at high concentration	Very exothermic reaction, producing a very concentrated ammonium nitrate product
In Laboratory	Titration and crystallisation at lower concentrations	Slow reaction, producing pure ammonium nitrate crystals

Sources of Potassium and Phosphorus

Potassium chloride and potassium sulfate are mined and used as a source of potassium.

Phosphate rock can also be mined, but must be reacted with acid to produce soluble phosphate salts.

Phosphate rock + ...	Products
Nitric acid	Phosphoric acid and calcium nitrate
Sulfuric acid	Calcium sulfate and calcium phosphate
Phosphoric acid	Calcium phosphate

Yusuf is really into his phosphate rock.

Required Practicals 1

Making Soluble Salts

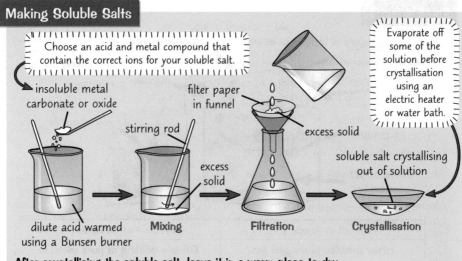

Choose an acid and metal compound that contain the correct ions for your soluble salt.

Evaporate off some of the solution before crystallisation using an electric heater or water bath.

insoluble metal carbonate or oxide

filter paper in funnel

excess solid

stirring rod

excess solid

soluble salt crystallising out of solution

dilute acid warmed using a Bunsen burner

Mixing   Filtration   Crystallisation

After crystallising the soluble salt, leave it in a warm place to dry.

Titrations

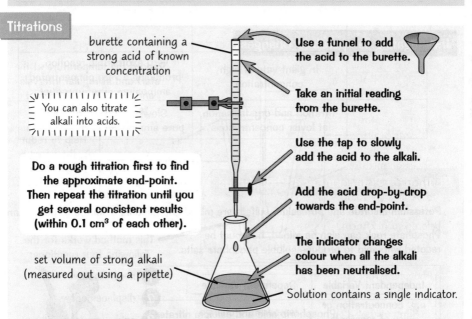

burette containing a strong acid of known concentration

Use a funnel to add the acid to the burette.

You can also titrate alkali into acids.

Take an initial reading from the burette.

Use the tap to slowly add the acid to the alkali.

Do a rough titration first to find the approximate end-point. Then repeat the titration until you get several consistent results (within 0.1 cm³ of each other).

Add the acid drop-by-drop towards the end-point.

The indicator changes colour when all the alkali has been neutralised.

set volume of strong alkali (measured out using a pipette)

Solution contains a single indicator.

Take another reading and calculate the volume added at the end-point:

Volume of acid added is difference between the two readings.

Then you can use your data to calculate the concentration of the alkali.

Required Practicals 2

Electrolysis

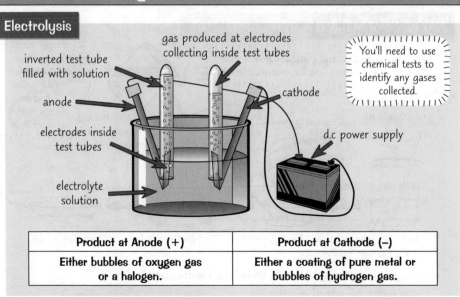

inverted test tube filled with solution

gas produced at electrodes collecting inside test tubes

You'll need to use chemical tests to identify any gases collected.

anode

cathode

electrodes inside test tubes

d.c power supply

electrolyte solution

Product at Anode (+)	Product at Cathode (–)
Either bubbles of oxygen gas or a halogen.	Either a coating of pure metal or bubbles of hydrogen gas.

Investigating Temperature Changes

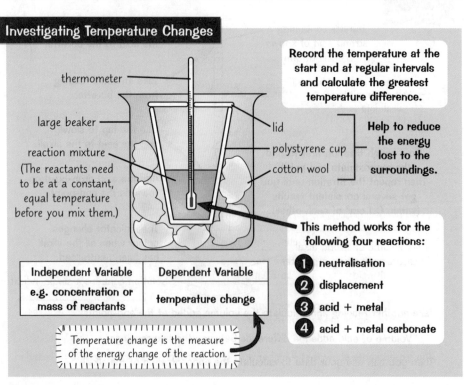

thermometer

large beaker

reaction mixture
(The reactants need to be at a constant, equal temperature before you mix them.)

lid

polystyrene cup

cotton wool

Record the temperature at the start and at regular intervals and calculate the greatest temperature difference.

Help to reduce the energy lost to the surroundings.

This method works for the following four reactions:

1. neutralisation
2. displacement
3. acid + metal
4. acid + metal carbonate

Independent Variable	Dependent Variable
e.g. concentration or mass of reactants	temperature change

Temperature change is the measure of the energy change of the reaction.

Required Practicals

Required Practicals 3

Two Ways of Measuring Rates of Reaction

① **The volume of gas given off**

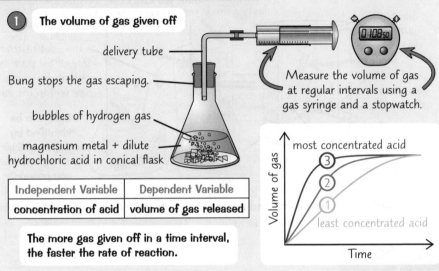

delivery tube

Bung stops the gas escaping.

bubbles of hydrogen gas

magnesium metal + dilute hydrochloric acid in conical flask

Measure the volume of gas at regular intervals using a gas syringe and a stopwatch.

most concentrated acid

least concentrated acid

Volume of gas

Time

Independent Variable	Dependent Variable
concentration of acid	volume of gas released

The more gas given off in a time interval, the faster the rate of reaction.

② **Precipitation**

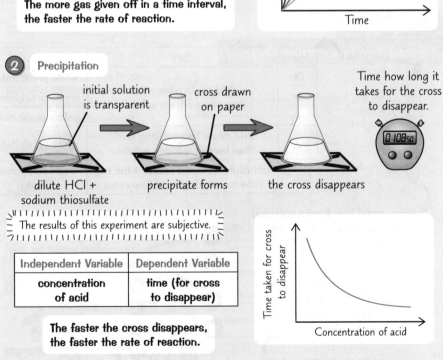

initial solution is transparent

cross drawn on paper

Time how long it takes for the cross to disappear.

dilute HCl + sodium thiosulfate

precipitate forms

the cross disappears

The results of this experiment are subjective.

Independent Variable	Dependent Variable
concentration of acid	time (for cross to disappear)

Time taken for cross to disappear

Concentration of acid

The faster the cross disappears, the faster the rate of reaction.

The experiments show that a higher acid concentration gives a faster rate of reaction.

Required Practicals 4

Paper Chromatography

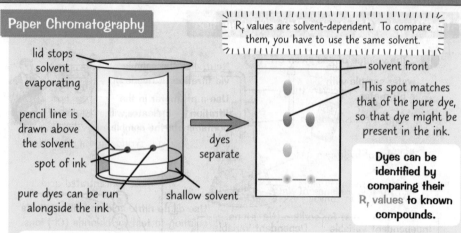

R$_f$ values are solvent-dependent. To compare them, you have to use the same solvent.

lid stops solvent evaporating

pencil line is drawn above the solvent

spot of ink

pure dyes can be run alongside the ink

dyes separate

shallow solvent

solvent front

This spot matches that of the pure dye, so that dye might be present in the ink.

Dyes can be identified by comparing their R$_f$ values to known compounds.

The experiment should be repeated to see if the spots still match in different solvents.

Identifying Ions

dropping pipette

Add a few drops of reagent.

mystery solution

Anion	Test	Observation
Cl⁻	Add dilute nitric acid, then silver nitrate solution	white precipitate
Br⁻		cream precipitate
I⁻		yellow precipitate
SO_4^{2-}	Add dilute hydrochloric acid, then barium chloride solution	white precipitate
CO_3^{2-}	Add dilute acid and connect the test tube to a test tube of limewater.	limewater turns cloudy

Some metal ions form a coloured precipitate with NaOH solution.

Ca^{2+}	white
Cu^{2+}	blue
Fe^{2+}	green
Fe^{3+}	brown
Mg^{2+}	white
Al^{3+}	white

Precipitate redissolves in excess NaOH to form a colourless solution.

Four steps for performing flame tests

1. Dip a platinum wire loop in dilute HCl.

2. Hold it in a blue Bunsen flame until it burns without colour.

3. Dip the loop into the sample.

4. Hold the loop in the flame.

Li⁺	Na⁺	K⁺	Ca^{2+}	Cu^{2+}
crimson	yellow	lilac	orange-red	green

Required Practicals 5

Five Steps for the Purification of Water

1 Test the pH of the water sample with a pH meter.

2 Neutralise the sample via titration (if needed).

Use a pH meter in the titration — indicator will contaminate the sample.

The sample has been neutralised.

3 Test for the presence of NaCl.

Do a flame test for sodium (Na^+) ions.

yellow flame

Use dilute nitric acid and silver nitrate solution to test for chloride (Cl^-) ions.

white precipitate

4 Distil the sample.

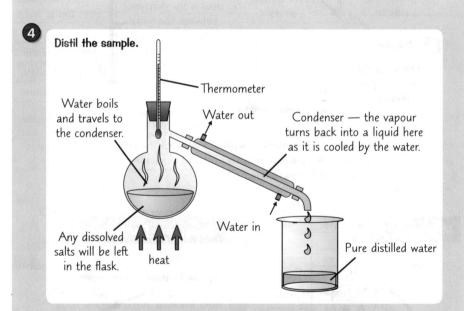

Thermometer

Water boils and travels to the condenser.

Water out

Condenser — the vapour turns back into a liquid here as it is cooled by the water.

Any dissolved salts will be left in the flask.

heat

Water in

Pure distilled water

5 Retest the pH of the distilled water, and for the presence of NaCl.

Apparatus and Techniques

Measuring Mass

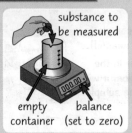

substance to be measured

empty container   balance (set to zero)

Transferring solid to reaction vessel:

 When making a solution, wash remaining solid out of the weighing container with the solvent you're dissolving it in.

or

 Find the difference in mass of the container and its contents before and after you transfer the solid.

Three Ways to Measure Liquids

1 **Pipette**

pipette filler (draws up liquid)

transfers accurate volumes

graduated pipette

calibrated to reduce transfer errors

3 **Measuring cylinder**

Pick a suitable size for volume required.

2 **Burette**

Volume of liquid used is the difference between the initial and final readings on the scale.

scale measures from top to bottom

tap releases liquid into a container

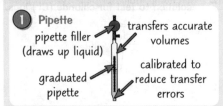

When measuring volumes of liquids: Always read the volume from the bottom of the meniscus.

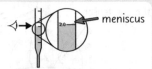 meniscus

Measuring Time

stopwatch

stopwatches are sensitive

start and stop the timer at the exact right time

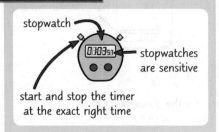

Measuring Temperature

wait for temperature to stabilise

thermometer

bulb fully submerged

read off scale at eye level

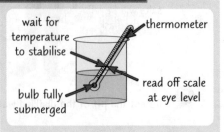

Practical Techniques

Measuring pH

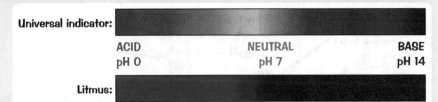

Universal indicator:		
ACID	NEUTRAL	BASE
pH 0	pH 7	pH 14

Litmus:

Indicator solution	Indicator paper
Changes colour of whole solution	For testing a few drops of solution
Good for showing the end-point in titrations	Use damp indicator paper to test gases

pH probes **and** pH meters
give a numerical value for pH.

pH meter

pH probe

Safety Precautions

Read the safety precautions to do with your method before you start any experiment.

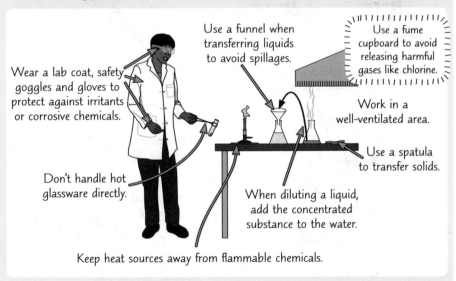

Use a funnel when transferring liquids to avoid spillages.

Use a fume cupboard to avoid releasing harmful gases like chlorine.

Wear a lab coat, safety goggles and gloves to protect against irritants or corrosive chemicals.

Work in a well-ventilated area.

Use a spatula to transfer solids.

Don't handle hot glassware directly.

When diluting a liquid, add the concentrated substance to the water.

Keep heat sources away from flammable chemicals.

Practical Skills

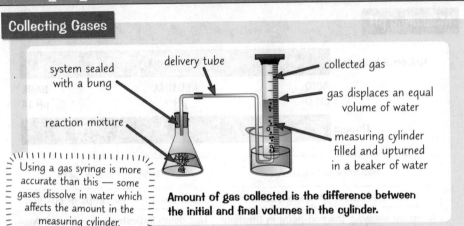

Equipment and Heating Substances

Collecting Gases

system sealed with a bung

delivery tube

collected gas

gas displaces an equal volume of water

reaction mixture

measuring cylinder filled and upturned in a beaker of water

Using a gas syringe is more accurate than this — some gases dissolve in water which affects the amount in the measuring cylinder.

Amount of gas collected is the difference between the initial and final volumes in the cylinder.

Using Bunsen Burners

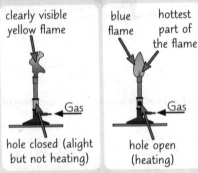

clearly visible yellow flame

blue flame

hottest part of the flame

Gas

Gas

hole closed (alight but not heating)

hole open (heating)

You can use scientific drawings to show how apparatus is set up:

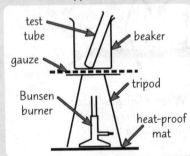

test tube

beaker

gauze

tripod

Bunsen burner

heat-proof mat

Other Heating Methods

Water bath

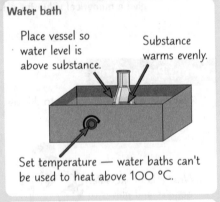

Place vessel so water level is above substance.

Substance warms evenly.

Set temperature — water baths can't be used to heat above 100 °C.

Electric heater

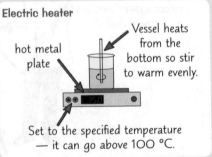

Vessel heats from the bottom so stir to warm evenly.

hot metal plate

Set to the specified temperature — it can go above 100 °C.

CAN041

Yay! You've only gone and made it through ALL the facts. Give yourself a round of applause.

Practical Skills